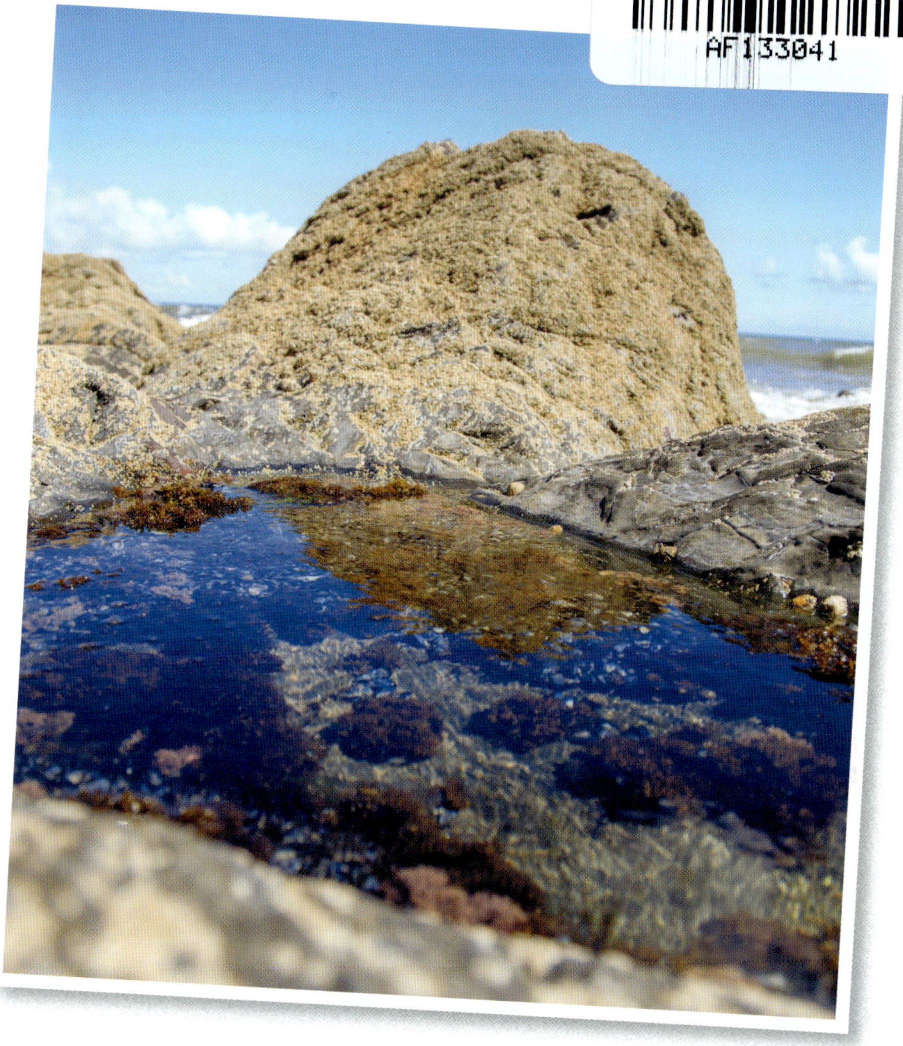

In the rock pool...

we see shells

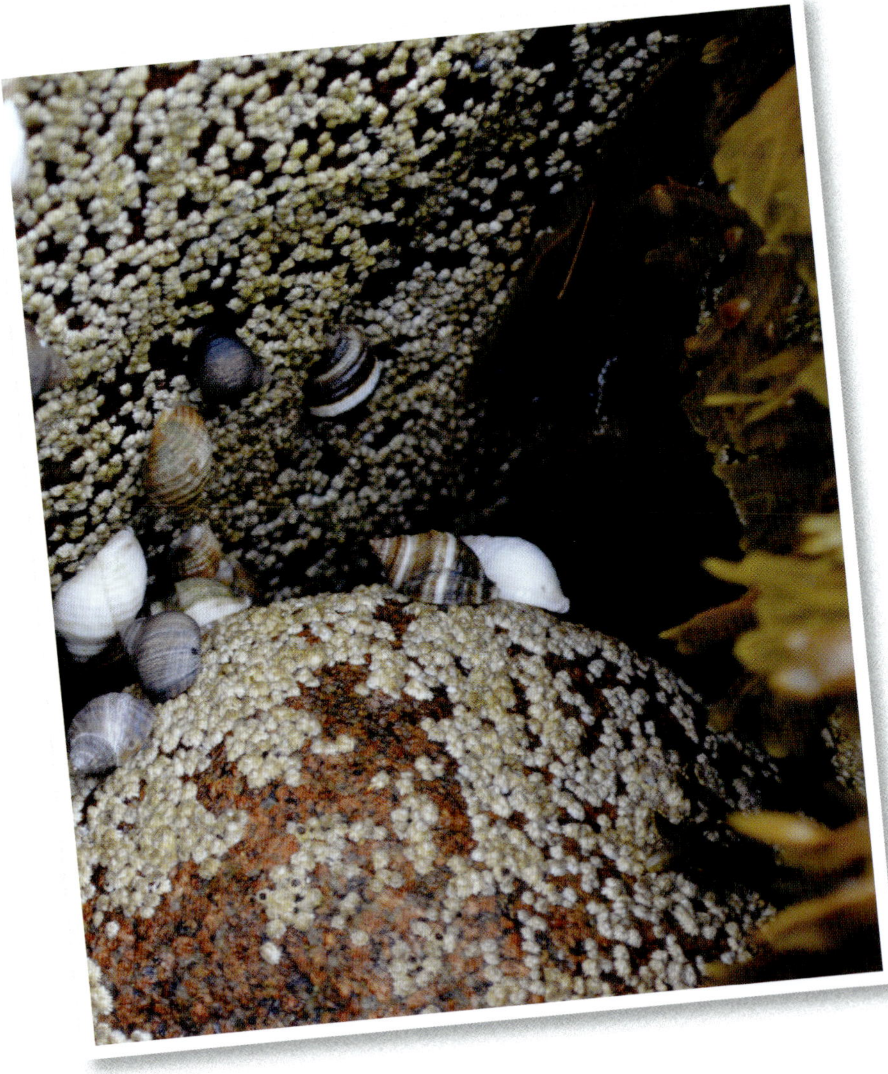

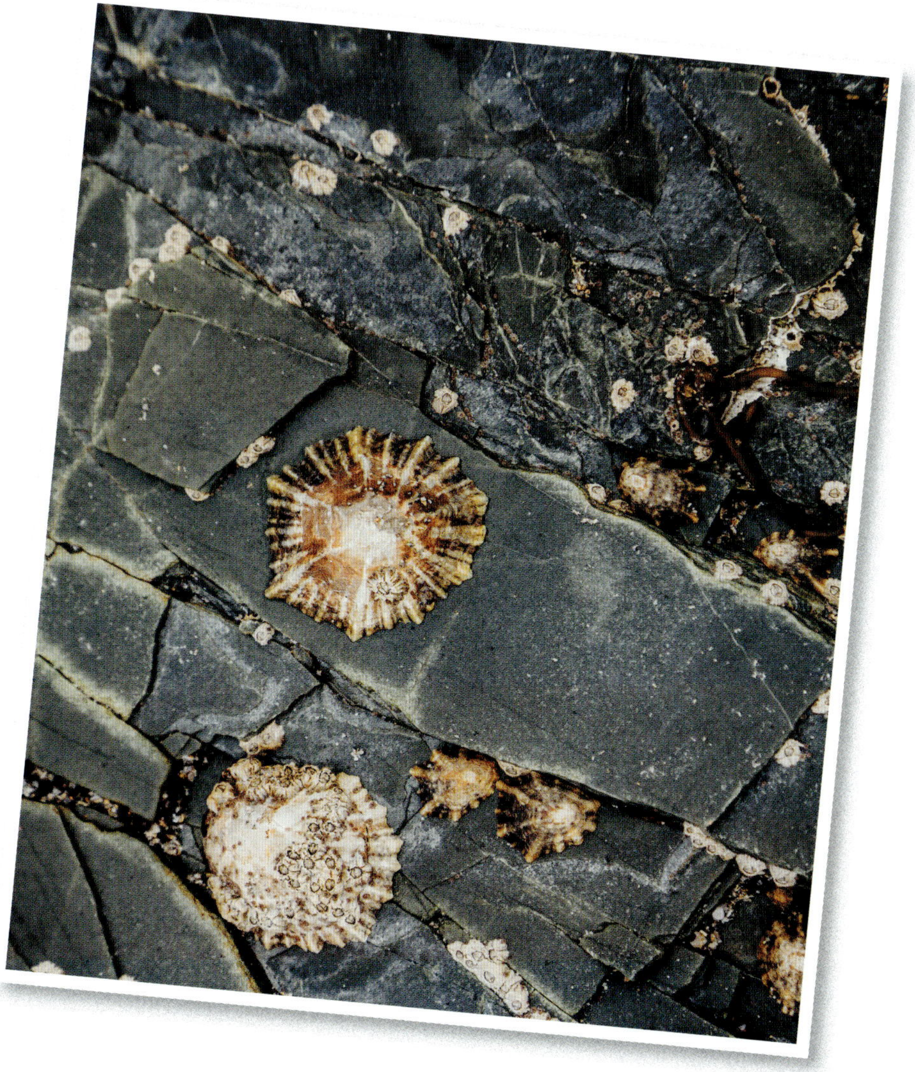

and limpets.

In the weeds...

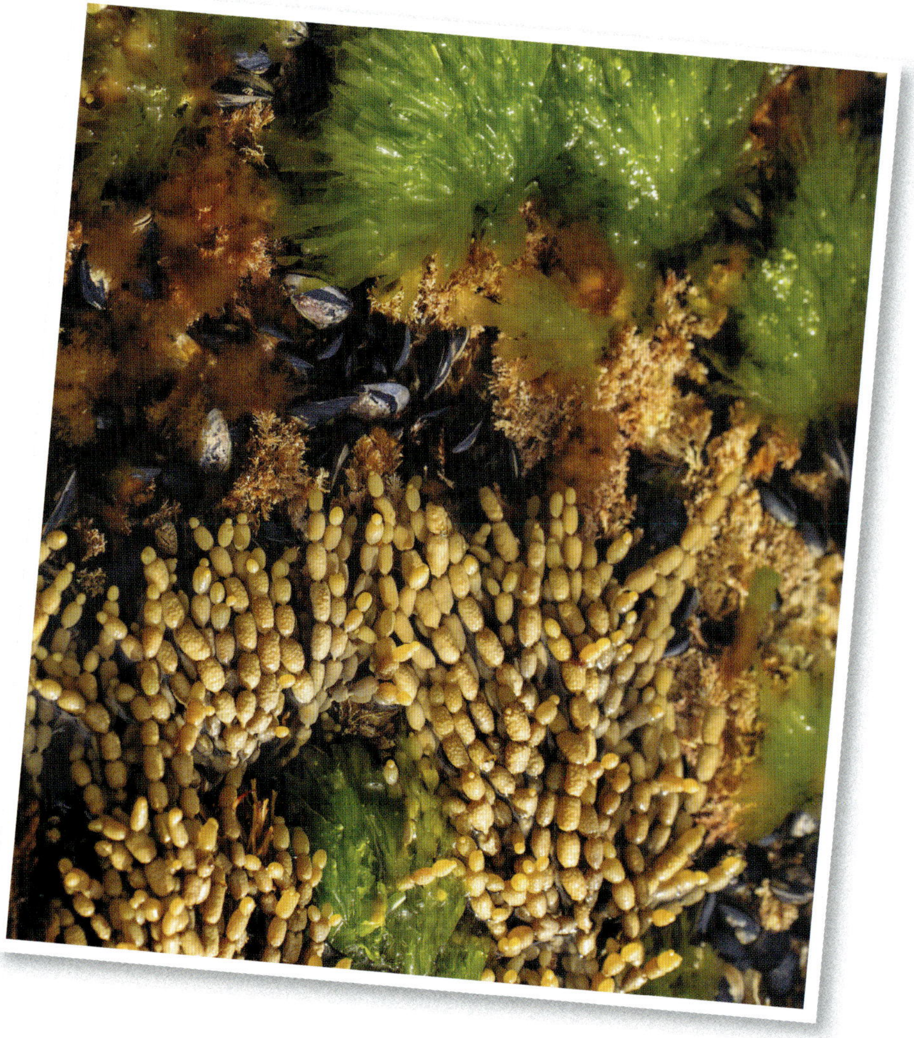

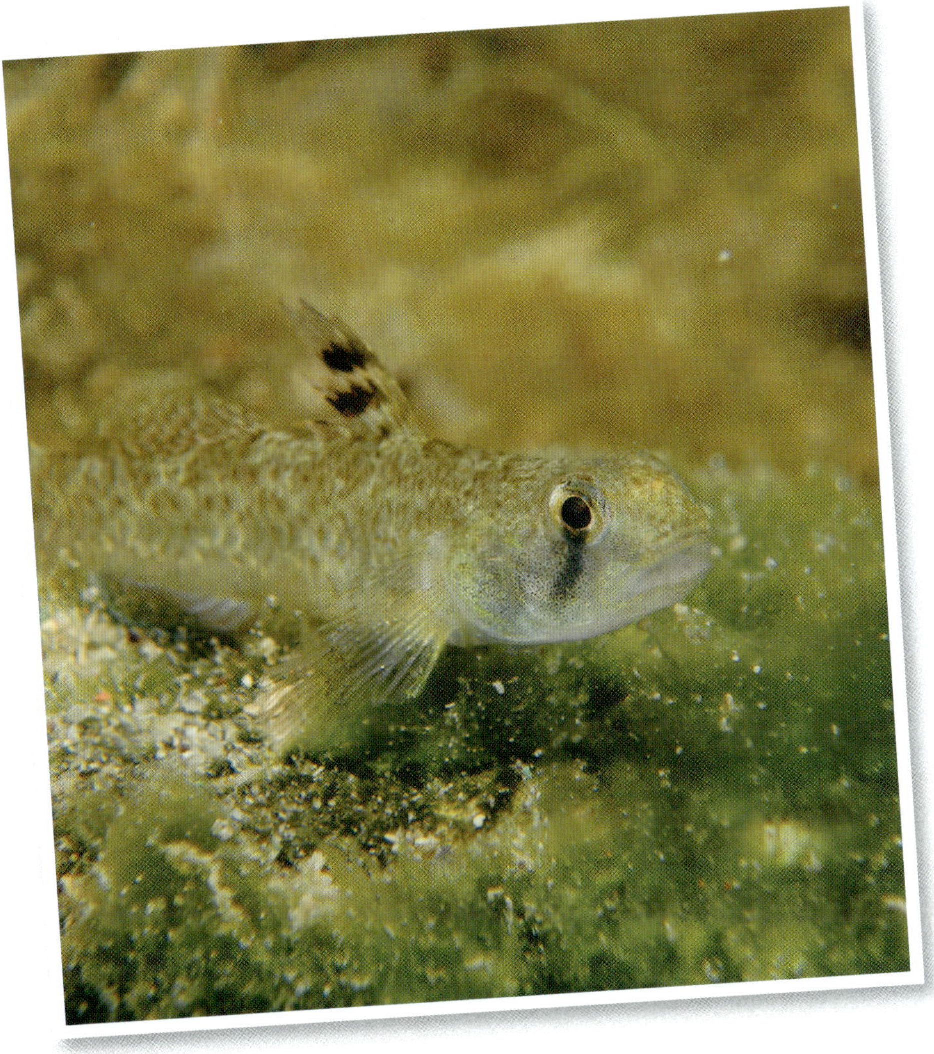

a fish...

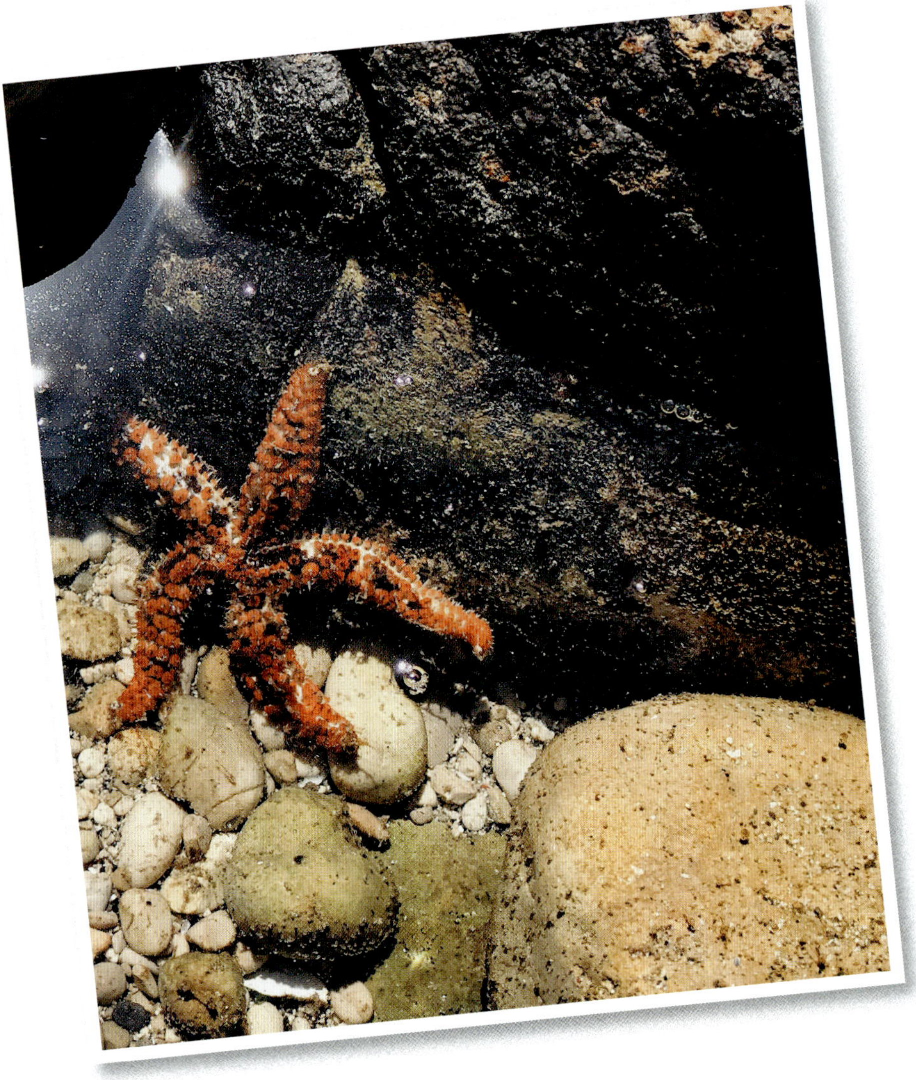

and a starfish.

Under the rocks...

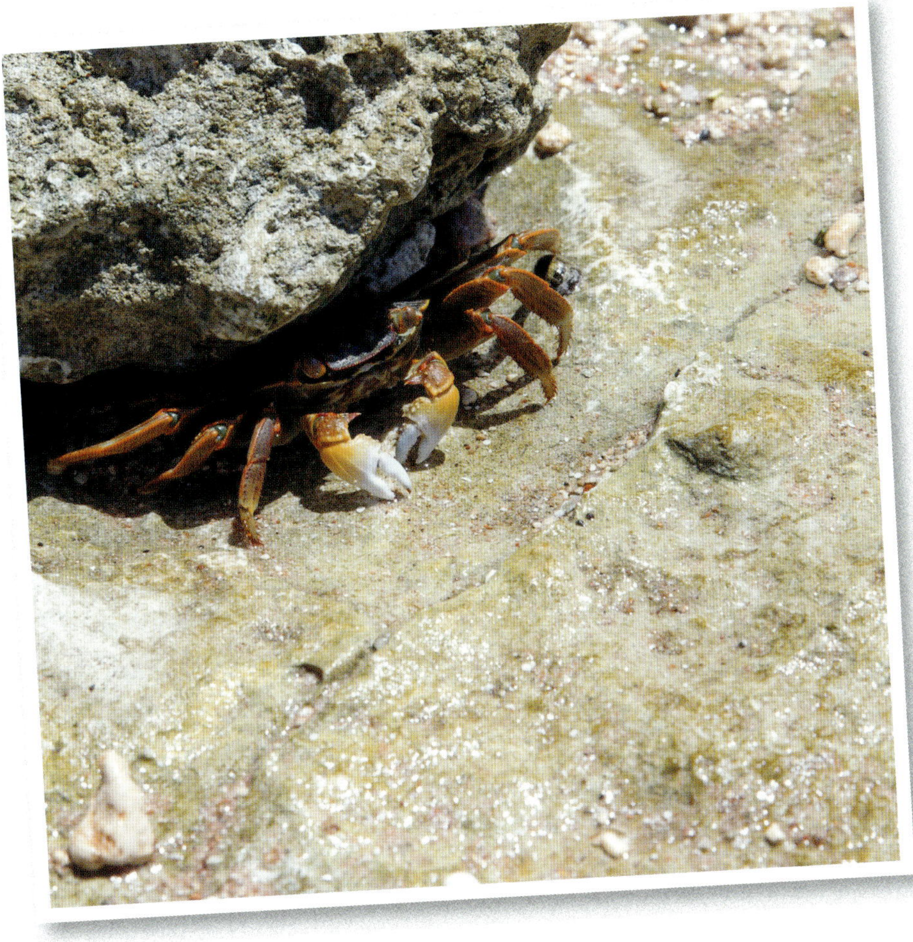

a crab!

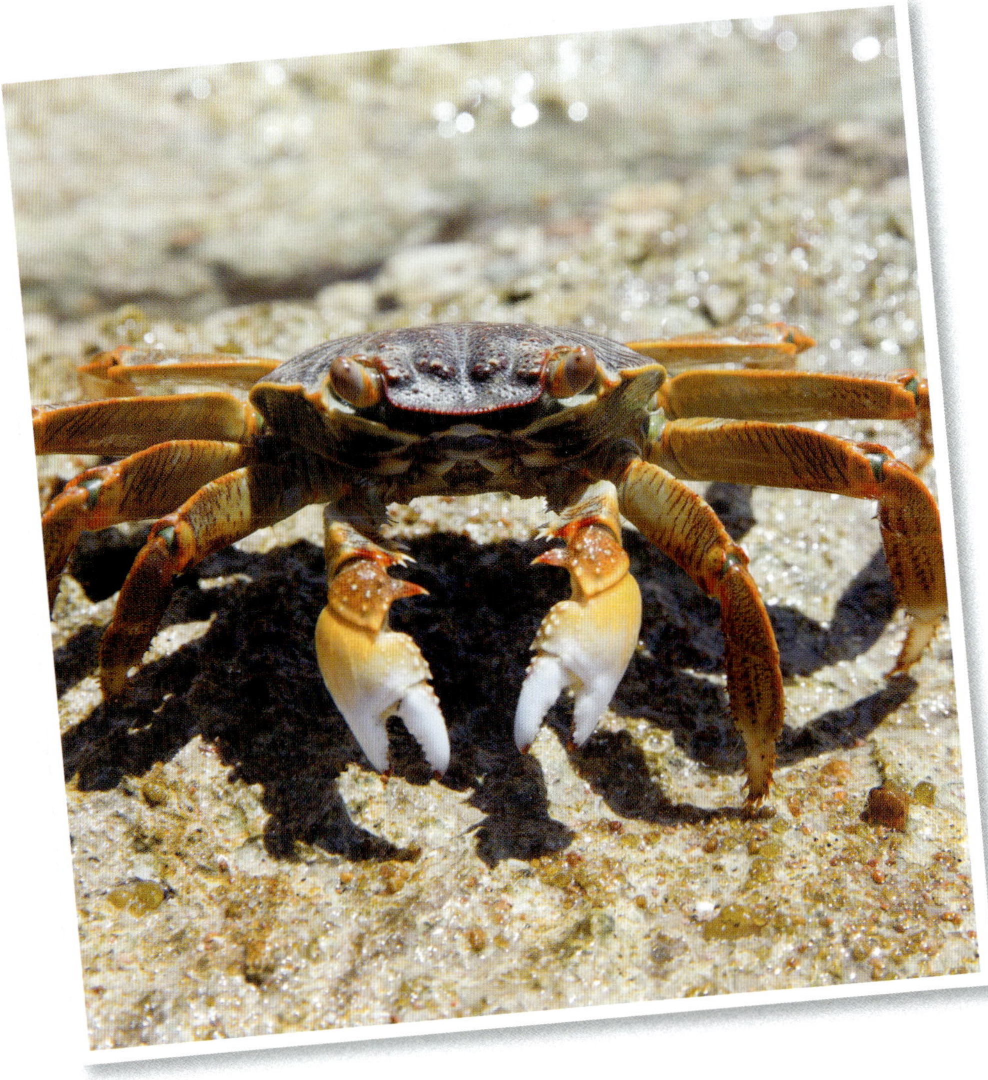